WILLIAM M. GAINES'S

THE ORGANIZATION MAD

Albert B. Feldstein, Editor

A SIGNET BOOK from
NEW AMERICAN LIBRARY
TIMES MIRROR
New York and Scarborough, Ontario
The New English Library Limited, London

Published as a SIGNET BOOK by arrangement with E. C. Publications, Inc., who have authorized this softcover edition.

Eighteenth Printing

SIGNET TRADEMARK REG. U.S. PAT. OFF. AND FOREIGN COUNTRIES
REGISTERED TRADEMARK—MARCA REGISTRADA
HECHO EN CHICAGO, U.S.A.

Signet, Signet Classics, Signette, Mentor and Plume Books are published *in the United States* by The New American Library, Inc., 1301 Avenue of the Americas, New York, New York 10019, *in Canada* by The New American Library of Canada Limited, 81 Mack Avenue, Scarborough, 704, Ontario, *in the United Kingdom* by The New English Library Limited, Barnard's Inn, Holborn, London, E.C. 1, England.

PRINTED IN THE UNITED STATES OF AMERICA

YOU ARE ABOUT TO MEET . . .

THE ORGANIZATION MAD

Other organizations glamorize "The Influential" . . .
The Organization MAD glamorizes "The Nonessential!"

Other publications make use of "Snob Appeal" . . .
MAD publications make use of "Slob Appeal!"

Other outfits consist of "Status-Seekers" . . .
The MAD outfit consists of "Status-Tweakers!"

The accepted dress elsewhere is
"The Gray Flannel Suit" . . .

The accepted dress at MAD is
"The Gray Flannel Sweatshirt!"

Other approaches usually border upon the subliminal . . .
The MAD approach usually borders upon the criminal!

YES, ONCE YOU'RE EXPOSED TO . . .
THE ORGANIZATION MAD
. . . YOU'LL NEVER BE THE SAME AGAIN!

SO, IF YOU HAVEN'T PAID FOR THIS BOOK,
THERE'S STILL TIME TO PUT IT BACK . . .
AND REMAIN A MISERABLE, UNHAPPY CLOD!

CONTENTS

TV Department
Dizzyland . . . 6
Newspapers Department
Item . . . 22
Hollywood Department—I
A Scene We'd Like to See . . . 30
Sports Department
Bowling . . . 35
Soft-Sell Advertising Department—I . . . 48
Out of Order Department
Vending Machines of the Future . . . 54
Poison Ivy Department
Camp . . . 64
Section 8 Department
Why I Left the Army . . . 78
Shopping Department
Super-Duper Markets . . . 87
Literary Movie Department
Morbid Dick . . . 88
Comparison Proves Department
Products for TV Commercials . . . 100
Oh, Promise Me Department
Wedding Album . . . 109
Adult Western Department
Gunsmoked . . . 118
Hollywood Department—II
Another Scene We'd Like to See . . . 136
Business Department
Success Story . . . 142
Spoil-Sports Department
Baseball's Hall of Shame! . . . 154
Having a Ball Department
High-School Dance . . . 162
Home-Sweet-Homes Department
Real Estate Ads . . . 178
Soft-Sell Advertising Department—II . . . 186

TV DEPT.

MAD'S VERSION OF

AND NOW, HERE IS HOST WALT DIZZY,

A BIG, BIG! TV SHOW...

WHO USUALLY INTRODUCES DIZZYLAND

This scrap-book contains many fond memories for me. For example, it contains scenes from my first animated cartoon... er...now...what *was* that title?
U. NO.
HOO

This scrap-book also contains scenes from my first feature-length animated movie, "Snow... something..." The title slips my mind at the moment...
OOOPS!

Heh, Heh! *Wrong scrap-book!* This scrap-book contains the first dollar I ever made, U.S. silver certificate, series of 1920, Serial No. A-5017234-J!

Making animated cartoons is an exacting art. It takes roughly 50,000 separate cells or drawings to make one cartoon. I keep a set of 50,000 cells in each of these drawers . . .
TOP
SECRET
KEEP OUT

For example, this drawer contains the 50,000 cells I made for my first Darnold Duck cartoon back in nineteen thirty . . .
OOOPS!

Heh, Heh! *Wrong drawer!* This drawer contains the 50,000 bills my first Darnold Duck cartoon made for me!

In this cabinet are the intricate models I made for my feature movie "20,000 Grand...er... LEAGUES under the . . ." OOOPS! *Wrong cabinet!*

Quick! Let's switch to Jimmy Dood in the Music Room!—Say, that's not Jimmy Dood! OOOPS! *WRONG ROOM!*
M

VIVID

A broken promise of things to come.

INFORMATIVE Tomorrowsland feature depicts history of rockets starting with invention as novel toy by Ancient Chinese and shows honorable inventors having much honorable fun . . .

FEATURE TRACES development from novel toy to have honorable fun with to first practical use with interesting attempt to send the mail via rockets in early nineteen-twenties.

STORY TRACES ROCKET DEVELOPMENT FROM NOVEL TOY TO PRESENT DAY

FEATURE GOES ON to show how novel toy to have honorable fun with was developed by Germans during World War II into effective weapon of dishonorable 'fun,' the dreaded V-2.

FEATURE COMES up to date by showing scientists at White Sands making countless experimental launchings of latest rocket types. By George...! We're back having honorable fun...

EXPLOITS

True tales made up from the legendary past.

Competition

TRADITIONAL AMERICAN SPIRIT of competition is conveyed durin exciting keelboat race as raggle-taggle crews of Davy Crawcut and Mike Finque eagerly pole their way down Mississippi River

OF PIONEER HEROES TEACH TODAY'S YOUTH RESPECT FOR AMERICAN TRADITIONS

Sportsmanship

GOOD OLD AMERICAN sportsmanship tradition is shown by Davy Crawcutt when he fails to shoot ale cup off Mike's head.

The wonderland of Nature's own film.

REAL-LIVE

OZGOOD ZEISS, Dizzyland Real-Live Adventures ace cameraman perches on mountain ledge, awaits rare appearance of the never-before-photographed Ring-Necked Fuzzwort.

CAMERA READY, Ozgood waits... and waits. Summer wanes, Autumn leaves begin to fall, and Winter snows begin, but still no Fuzzwort. Determined Ozgood clings to perch.

ADVENTURES CAMERAMAN WAITS YEAR FOR SHOT OF RARE BIRD

SPRING THAW comes, and one year passes. Finally, after twenty month vigil, Fuzzwort makes appearance. Jubilant Ozgood takes history making chance-of-a-lifetime shot . . .

THEN, as Fuzzwort disappears again, Ozgood flings himself screaming from ledge, realizing that chance-of-a-lifetime shot is ruined. Dated film in camera had expired . . .

The happiest world of them all—for kids.

THE

The happiest world of them all?!?

What's so happy about it?

Actually we're *miserable!*

Don't get the idea because we're drawn smiling, we're happy!

HAPPIEST WORLD OF THEM ALL

Now he pushes us aside!
...in favor of movies with REAL LIVE ANIMALS...and REAL LIVE PEOPLE!
Sometimes he even makes us *act* in them!

Walt may tell you he's doing it mainly to try out new things...
Walt may tell you he's doing it mainly for kicks!
The truth is...
...he's doing it mainly for *money!*

NEWSPAPERS DEPT.

item

Billy Poobah, son of Mr. & Mrs. Jim Poobah, took a bicycle ride yesterday. But imagine his surprise when he returned home to find his father waiting for him with a hairbrush. It seems that the bike Billy took for a ride wasn't his. It belonged to the little boy next door.

The other day, while perusing pages of a little-known weekly paper called "The Abilene Gardening Club and P.T.A. Gazette," we ran across the above story . . . and it started us thinking. What would happen if this story were picked up by the wire services and sent around the country? Here's MAD's version of how some newspapers, magazines and columnists would treat it:

As Pegler Sees It:

A Delinquent Chip off the Old Blockhead

By WESTBROOK PEGLER

I SEE they finally caught up with this guy, this Billy whatzisname, this Poobah whack out in Kansas. But what doesn't surprise me and shouldn't surprise anybody who got out of the sixth grade on his own hook and has half a brain for what's going on and isn't a bunch of dopes is that it's this same Poobah character whose old man was a charter member of the Roosevelt-Truman-Juan Peron-Falange, that carried the citizens of Abeline, along with their votes, in its hip pocket for so long.

And it's the same Poobah, the old man this time, who under cover of being a janitor in one of those egg-head high schools, carried wastebaskets for years in one hand, and his party membership card in the other. And you know what I think of Eleanor Roosevelt.

Before janitor, this slob was a patrol leader in Boy Scout Troop 18, the notorious commy-front group I exposed last Christmas Eve.

It was his old lady who used to bake cookies for the Salvation Army's Send-a-Boy-to-Camp Movement, (alias the Abraham Lincoln Brigade), the same summer camp, you recall, which brought together such commy-loving cronies as you know what I think of Eleanor Roosevelt.

It stinks. The whole thing stinks. You stink.

HOLLYWOOD HIGHLIGHTS

Epic Crime To Be Movie Epic

By LOUELLA O. PARSONS

Motion Picture Editor, International News Service

SNAPSHOTZ OF HOLLYWOOD COLLECTED AT RANDOM . . . Well folks, all Movieland is agog. Because underneath all that tinsel and glamour, people here are just like folks. What I'm trying to tell you is William Wyler stopped by my house this morning on the way to the studio because, as Bill put it, he couldn't wait to tell me the happy news.

Charles Bickford

So here is the exclusive news Bill told me over a cup of coffee in the kitchen. He has purchased the exclusive rights to the "Billy Poobah Story". That was the story you will recall, of the little boy out in Joplin, St. Louis, who stole a bicycle and did all those terrible things. Bill also wanted me to know exclusively that he has lined up Sal Mineo to play Billy, and, of course, June Alyson will play Billy's mother. Charles Bickford, that wonderful old character actor, will play Billy's bicycle.

DAILY NEWS

NEW YORK'S PICTURE NEWSPAPER®

Billy (The Kid) Yields In Daylight Nab

Abeline, Aug. 16 — For sex hours today, citizens of Abeline, shocked by one of the most bizarre crimes committed in these parts since the bawdy, sexy, early frontier days, waited for the capture of the hopped-up, sex-crazed bicycle-thief, sex-year-old Billy Poobah.

The self-styled badman, wearing a Davy Crockett cap and a pair of faded, hand-me-down levis, was finally nabbed in his tree-house hideout along with several accomplices. (Latest reports fail to implicate any of these in the actual theft, although they are all being held as material witnesses.)

Gives up without a fight

Exhibiting the crooked sneer of the incorrigible juvenile delinquent, Billy Poobah was dragged, screaming, into his father's bedroom. (See photos in center fold). Through wild eyes, red-rimmed with debauchery, he looked out on what promised to be his last view of outside faces for at least sex days.

Sheriff refuses comment

The Sheriff's Office refused comment on whether or not Poobah was thought to be the mastermind behind a series of bicycle thefts and sex crimes which have terrorized Abeline for the past sex weeks.

(Compete with professionals! The NEWS *pays five dollars for on-the-spot newstips and unfounded rumors.)*

Lovely Vava Voom, starring in m
melting into cake of ice while sing
playing at your local theatre, so y

Daily Worker

Sharecropper's Son Victim Of International Banker's Plot

Abeline, Kan. Aug. 16 (TASS) — Once more, the hands of American Justice were tied, this time by a wolf-pack of insane, blood-hungry Capitalists, who stormed a rotted and battered farmhouse in the center of the great Kansas Dust Bowl, and with savage screams of "Kill the peasant!", dragged out onto the cropless dry earth the broken and mutilated body of little comrade Billy Poobah.

With typical American Capitalist decadent mob-rule efficiency, they kicked the peasant child as far as the nearest leafless tree, and there, in the words of the popular, pseudo-cowboy, movie-star-propagandists, they "strung him up" for his crime.

Comrade Billy Poobah's only crime was being poor.

This Thursday night, a Memorial Rally for Billy Poobah will be held in Madison Square Garden. Paul Robeson will sing "The Ballad of Billy Poobah", and a collection will be made. Don't fail to attend. Don't fail to bring money.

EDITORIAL PAGE

Journal NEW YORK American

"The end of everything is the beginning of nothing."

—William Randolph Hearst

An Open Letter To Billy Poobah

WE'VE NEVER met you, Billy. You may be short, or tall, or fat, or thin, or all those things. We don't know. We may even like you. Someday.

BUT NOT TODAY!

NO, BILLY. Not today. For today, you are an angry man, full of the stone-headed UNREASONABLENESS that has cursed all the angry men who have gone before you.

THE NAPOLEONS, THE HITLERS, THE STALINS, THE ROOSEVELTS!

WE KNOW your crime, Billy. And somehow, we feel that tomorrow, you will regret that crime. AT LEAST WE HOPE YOU DO! For stone-headed UNREASONABLENESS can never contend with TRUTH and HONESTY and SINCERITY and LOVE and HONOR and AMERICANISM.

NOT FOR LONG!

SO TRY, Billy. Try for a moment to look across your narrow road, and see what's on the other side. See what you've done to the people on the other side of that road. See how you have hurt those people . . . PEOPLE WHO LOVE YOU, IN SPITE OF THAT HURT.

WE'VE NEVER met you, Billy. But someday, we may even like you.

THE AMERICAN PEOPLE

TIME

THE WEEKLY NEWSMAGAZINE

THE NATION

For Billy, No Santa Claus

Out on the hot, hard, dirt-caked streets of Abeline, Kansas, there was sadness today. For the first time in his brief life, little Billy Poobah (rhymes with Poo-Bah) knew the meaning of fear. Billy, who is short (2′6″), partly bald, and old beyond his thirty-seven months, was taken into custody on a charge of small theft. There, in the hot, hard, dirt-caked bedroom of his small Kansas farmhouse, Father Poobah prepared Billy for his Armageddon. (For Billy's reaction, see DOMESTIC AFFAIRS.)

The New York Times

BOY, THREE, HELD IN BIKE THEFT

Abeline Youth is Accused of Stealing New Bicycle by Neighbor's Boy

By ROBERT BUCK

Special to The New York Times.

ABELINE. Kan., Aug. 16 – It is alleged to have been reported by hitherto reliable but as yet unconfirmed sources. that a young man was indicted in Abeline. Kan., on a charge of third degree petty larceny. His name is being withheld. presumably pending investigation by proper authorities. This report has been neither confirmed nor denied by local officials.

HOLLYWOOD DEPT. I:

A SCENE WE'D LIKE TO SEE

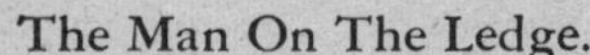
The Man On The Ledge.

JOE ORLANDO

SPORTS DEPT.

Where are those nice loving couples you used to see in the park each evening, walking hand-in-hand or smooching?

What's happened to those nice friendly folks you used to see in their homes every evening playing bridge or poker? Hah?

Where are they these evenings? Here's where they are! Indulging in the sport that enables them to unleash all their pent-up hostilities:

BOW
HOW ABOUT A TIP?

LING

CLOSE-UPS OF BOWLER SHOW

Ball leaves hand . . . Spins down alley . . . Hooks in sharply . . .

MAGIC-EYE CAMERA CATCHES

RELEASE OF PENT-UP EMOTION

pproaches pins . . . . A STRIKE!

PERFECT BOWLING ALLEY FORM

DIAGRAMS BELOW SHOW TYP

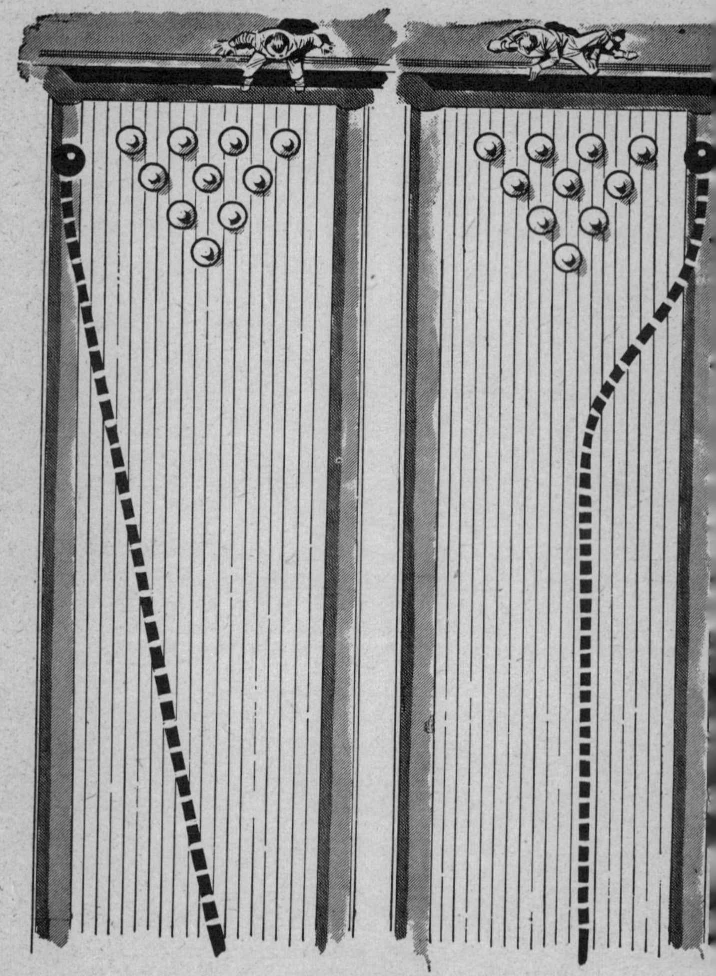

OF THROWS USED IN BOWLING

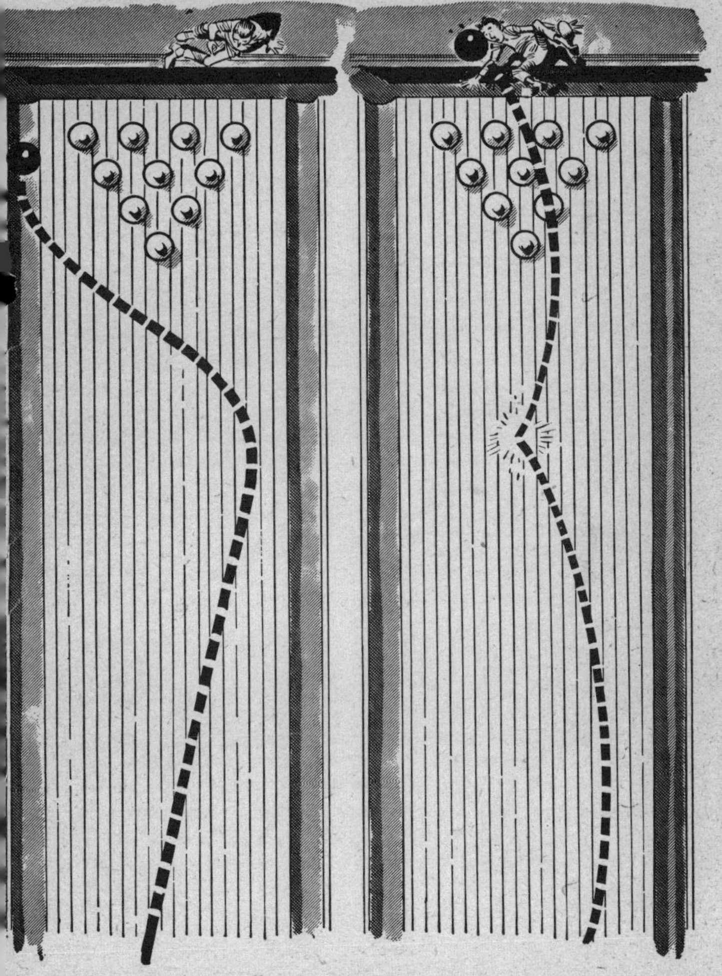

A SIMPLE OUTLINE

Scoring is a fascinating and enjoyable part of the game of bowling. If you know how to score, you are indeed fortunate, mainly because scoring gives you a chance to sit down. Here, then, is a brief simple outline of how to keep score. To make it even simpler, we have supplied a typical score (above) which you can follow while learning. Ready? Then here goes...

A game of bowling consists of ten innings, or frames. There are ten pins set up for each frame, and you have two balls, or chances to knock as many of them down as you can. If you knock down, say, seven pins with your two balls in the first frame, you put a seven in the first frame's big box. No, the little box is not for the score the midgets bowling in the next alley make, the little box is in case you make a spare or a strike. If you knock down all ten pins with your two balls, that is a spare. If you knock down all ten pins with your first ball, that is a strike. If you make a spare, you don't put anything down in the big box, you put a spare sign in the little box. This gives you ten pins plus the amount of pins you knock down with your next ball. If you get a strike, you put a strike sign in the little box, and this gives you ten pins plus the amount of pins you knock down with your next two balls. Thus, if you get a spare in the first frame, and you knock down eight pins with the first ball in the second frame, you can see that you get eighteen in the first frame. If you get a strike in the first frame and knock down nine pins with both balls in the second frame, you can see that you get nineteen in the first frame and nine more in the second frame, for a total of twenty-eight.

OF HOW TO SCORE IN BOWLING...

However, if you get ten pins with both balls in the second frame, you can see that this gives you twenty points in the first frame and a spare sign in the second frame, which means that in the second frame, you'll add ten points to the twenty in the first frame plus the amount of pins you knock down with the first ball in the third frame. Now, if you get a strike with the first ball in the second frame, and you already had a strike in the first frame, then you can't put anything down in the first frame because, as you can see, you still have another ball coming which won't be rolled till the third frame. Thus, the pins you knock down with that first ball in the third frame will be added to the ten pins you knocked down with the strike ball in the second frame, and all that will be added to the ten pins you knocked down with the strike ball in the first frame to give you your first frame's score. Then, the pins you knock down with the second ball you roll in the third frame will be added to the pins you knocked down with the first ball in the third frame, and that will be added to the ten pins you knocked down with the strike ball in the second frame which will be added to the score in the first frame to give you the score in the second frame. Now, if you happen to get a strike with the first ball you roll in the third frame, then you still owe one more ball to the second frame which won't be rolled till the fourth frame, and which will be the first of the two you owe to the third frame, and . . .

Well, as you can see, when it comes to scoring, here is one place where you can get rid of plenty pent-up hostility.

LEARNING TO BOWL

Lesson 1: Gripping the Ball

The bowling ball is gripped with 3 fingers, the middle finger, the index finger and the thumb, which fit into the 3 special holes provided.

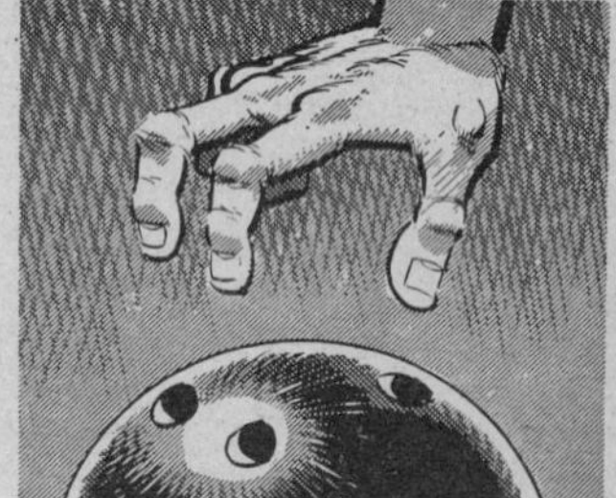

Hold hand with these three fingers pointing downward, fold the others back, approach ball rack, and slip fingers into holes in bowling ball.

Grasp bowling ball firmly and lift. You are now ready for the next important step in learning to bowl: The Approach. Carry ball . . . OOOPS!

One important thing we forgot to tell you about gripping the ball . . . Be sure your fingers aren't greasy . . . and that holes aren't too big!

Lesson 2: The Approach

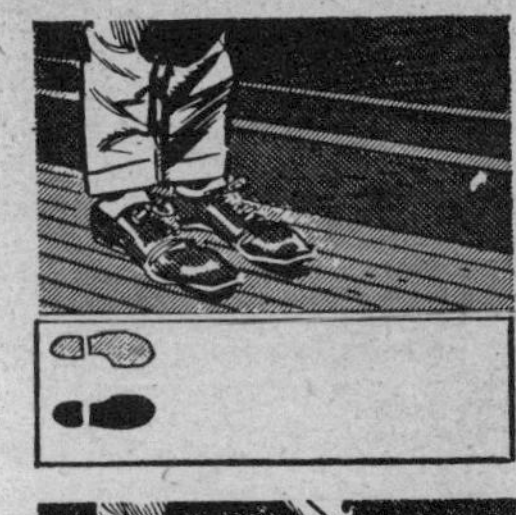

The important thing in the approach is to have perfect form. Start with feet together.

Now, take a 14-inch step with your left foot (1),

followed quickly by your right foot, stepping about twice that distance (2).

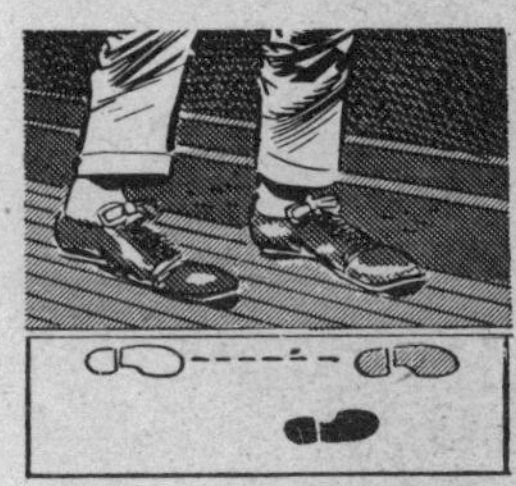

Slow up on the next left, which is another 14-inch step

Then cross over with your right foot, and slide on it.

You'll find this to be rather awkward for bowling, but on a dance floor, with the right music, it's a terrific Mambo!

FAMOUS RECORD HOLDERS IN BOWLI

JOHN L. LEWIS

Seventeen Strikes in a Row

TOMMY MANVILLE

Eleven Splits in a Row

OSGOOD Z'BEARD

Nineteen Pinboys in a Row

FAMILIAR BOWLING TERMS...

SPLIT

What happens when you go bowling in tight pants.

FOUL LINE

What you'll hear when you forget the pinboy's tip.

ALLEY

Where you'll sleep when you get home from bowling at 3 A.M.

SOFT-SELL ADVERTISING DEPT. I:

Time for the commercial, and a sickening example of what we're in for if the trend toward clever, humorous, soft-sell advertising continues.

A simple case of "recalcitrant plebney", Madam. Time for new, improved IRONEX TABLETS. Watch the amazing speed in which IRONEX brings comforting relief . . .

I'm afraid your husband is dead, Madam! He had worse than recalcitrant plebney. He had "plague"! We've got to get out of here . . . FAST!
Yes, Doctor, But . . . HOW?

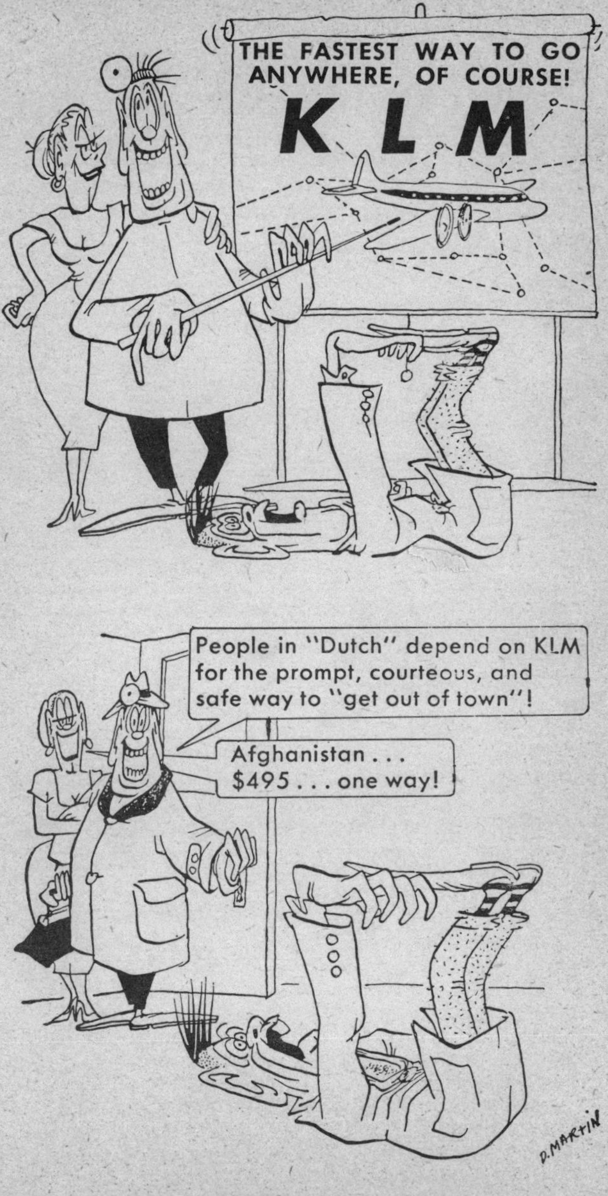

THE FASTEST WAY TO GO ANYWHERE, OF COURSE!

KLM

OUT OF ORDER DEPT.

During a lengthy survey taken over a cup of coffee the other morning, we came to the conclusion that you people owe a lot to vending machines. Just stop and think for a minute, all you people, of the functions these clever contraptions perform. They save steps. They give quicker service. They afford added convenience. And mainly, they throw countless people out of work. Yessiree, by George ... all

VEND
MACH
of the
FU

you unemployed people owe vending machines plenty!

Today, there seems to be a vending machine for almost every product: cigarettes, beverages, candy bars, axolotls, and halvah, to name just a few. But these are only the beginning. American ingenuity hasn't finished with them yet ...not by a long shot. Bigger and better vending machines are on the way. So here, then, is MAD's forecast of...

ING

INES

TURE

THE HAIR-O-MAT

Directions:

Deposit 76 Quarters, 9 Dimes, 1 Nickel and 3 Pennies.

1. Insert Coins
2. Press Button
3. Take out Toupee
4. Put it on, Idiot!

THE DOCT-O-MAT

Diagnosis............................Deposit 2,000 Pennies
Removal of Appendix..........Deposit 1,000 Dimes
30 Minute Psychoanalysis..Deposit 100 Quarters
Marital Advice.............................Free (if female)

D I R E C T I O N S

1. Insert Coins
2. Take off Clothes
3. Press Complaint Button
4. Read Remedy
5. Hit the Road!

COMPLAINT Press no more than two	**REMEDY** One may light up	
◎ Appendicitis	▣ Take it out	▣ Leave it in
◎ Itch	▣ Scratch	▣ Suffer
◎ Halitosis	▣ Don't talk	▣ Find New Friends
◎ Broken Leg	▣ Use other leg	▣ Break other leg
◎ Frammitis	▣ Tch! Tch!	▣ Hey! this is a family magazine!
◎ Dandruff	▣ Shampoo	▣ Toupee Machine over there

THE AUTO-VEND

A welcome future vending machine will be the one from which motorists will be able to purchase new cars. When these vending machines are worn out, they'll be classified as used vending machines and limited to dispensing used cars...

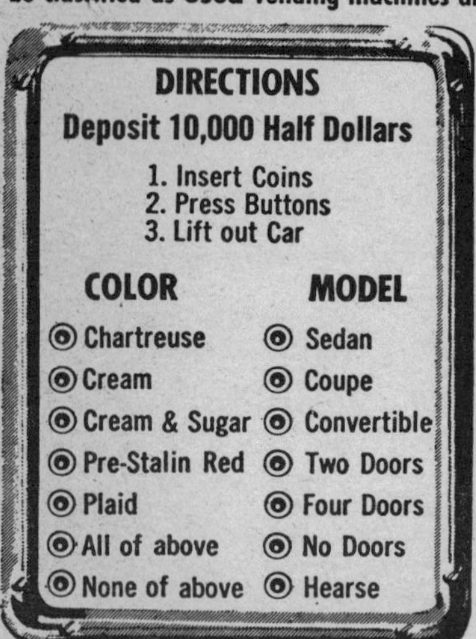

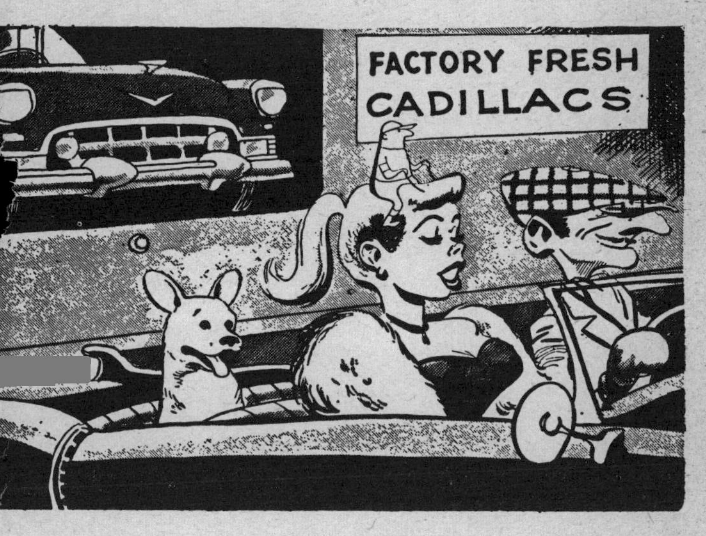
FACTORY FRESH
CADILLACS

THE WIFE-O-MAT

DIRECTIONS

Deposit 20 Half Dollars

1. Insert Coins
2. Show proof of non-married status (full wallet will do).
3. Select Specifications
4. Pucker Up
5. Wife will slide down chute

AGE Press One	SIZE Press One
◎ 18-21	◎ Sleek
◎ 22-30	◎ Pleasingly Plump
◎ 31-40	◎ Tapered
◎ 41-50	◎ Overripe
◎ Over 50	◎ Wow!
◎ Under 18 (good only in the hills)	◎ A Dog

DISPOSITION **Press One**	**INTELLIGENCE** **If you want any**
◎ Sweet	◎ Genius
◎ Moody	◎ Not Exactly
◎ Silent	◎ So-so
◎ Giggly	◎ Tries
◎ Obnoxious	◎ Addled
◎ Loathesome	◎ Idiot

THE VEND-A-BEAST

DIRECTIONS

1. Insert Coins
2. Press Button
3. Lift Window
4. Get out of the way!

◎ HORSE ....500 Dimes
◎ COW ....400 Dimes
◎ GOAT ....300 Dimes
◎ PIG ....200 Dimes
◎ CHICKEN ....100 Dimes
◎ HIRED HAND ......50 Dimes

THE VEND-O-VEND

Ultimate in future vending machines will be one which dispenses a vending machine. This in turn will dispense a vending machine, which will in turn dispense a vending machine, and so on. Final vending machine will dispense dime to be inserted in first vending machine and whole mess starts again . . .

POISON IVY DEPT.

EVERY SUMMER MILLIONS OF AMERICAN KIDS JUMP AT THE CHANCE TO DEVELOP SELF RELIANCE, COMMUNE WITH NATURE, GROW STRONG AND HEALTHY, LEARN TO SOCIALIZE, AND WRESTLE WITH THE PROBLEMS OF GROW-

ING UP. BUT MAINLY, THEY JUMP AT THE CHANCE TO GET AWAY FROM THEIR NAGGING PARENTS FOR TWO WHOLE MONTHS BY ESCAPING TO . . .

M P

SEWING ON NAME-TAPES IS MAIN PART OF CAMP SEASON'S PREPARATION

Prior to season, parents of camp-goer rush around buying required clothing and equipment. Then comes big job of sewing on name-tapes. Mama, Papa, Sister . . . even dog, Irving, sews on name-tapes. Couple in formal dress (right) are strangers who only stopped in to ask directions. . . .

Name-tape neatly sewn on Melvin Cowznofsky's tooth-brush.

Name-tape neatly sewn on Melvin Cowznofsky's tooth-paste.

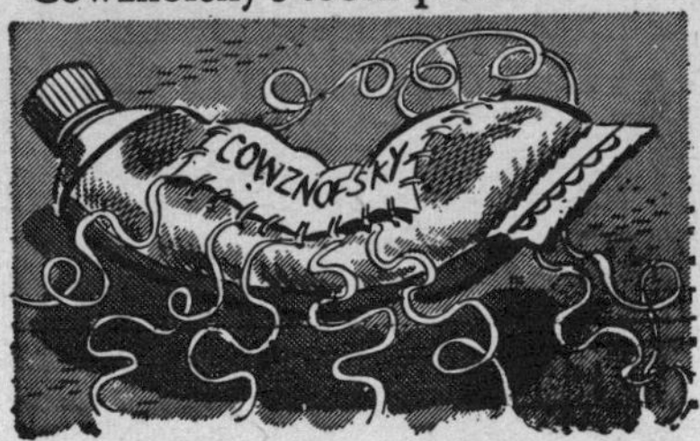

Name-tape neatly sewn on Melvin Cowznofsky's teeth . . .

TYPICAL GOING—AWAY SCENE
CAMP CARE FREE
INFORMATION
INFOR
3 3

TRACK 1
TRACK 3
CAMP MUGWUMP
CAMP POT-RA-ZEE-BEE
HORROR COMICS

CAMP ACTIVITIES BUILD SOUND

ARTS AND CRAFTS

OPPORTUNITY TO DEVELOP manual dexterity is offered campers by program of arts and crafts. Here, Melvin Cowznofsky proudly displays season project: leather wallet for father, equal in quality to those selling in stores for $2.50. Actual cost of wallet to Melvin's father, figuring in Melvin's camp fee: $175.00.

MINDS AND HEALTHY BODIES

WATER SPORTS

SWIMMING AND WATER SAFETY is taught POT-RA-ZEE-BEE campers by use of "buddy" system. When life-guard blows whistle and yells "buddies!", everybody must splash around and pair up with preassigned companion. (Obviously camper Cowznofsky, searching for drowned "buddy," has not yet learned water safety.)

DRAMATICS

SELF-EXPRESSION is learned by campers through participation in dramatic program. Here, Melvin Cowznofsky stages hysterical emotional scene to impress fellow-campers. Hysterical emotional scene being staged mainly because they refused Melvin part in camp play.

NATURE STUDY

CAMPER COWZNOFSKY joins outdoors study group using powerful field glasses to learn vital facts of Nature by observing migratory birds in trees overhead, odd animals in woods near by, and strange goings-on at resort hotel across lake. (Yessireeboy, there's plenty vital facts of Nature to be learned that way.)

CAMPER COWZNOFSKY AFT SUMMER OF SOUND MIND HEALTHY BODY-BUILDING . .

TYPICAL HOME-COMING SCENE

at railroad station on last day of cam season with parents crying and carryin on as they tearfully greet their childre with such admonitions as "Did yo change your socks?"; "Did you wa: behind your ears?"; "Did you eat?' and "Did you *have* to come home?' Touching concern kids are displaying sadness over realization that they mu say goodbye to summer camping con panions, sadness over realization th they must say farewell to summer joy but mainly sadness over realization th they face long hard winter with sam old nagging parents.

TRACK
1
TRACK
2
3
CAMP
POT
RA
ZEE
BEE

CAMP POT-RA-ZEE-BEE AFTER

AND HEALTHY BODY-

SUMMER OF SOUND MIND

BUILDING.

SECTION 8 DEPT.

WHY I LEFT THE ARMY AND BECAME A CIVILIAN

IN THE ARMY

. . . if I didn't get out of the sack at 6 A.M., my sergeant would blow his top!

AS A CIVILIAN

. . . I enjoy the luxury of sleeping as long as I want and getting up when I feel like it.

IN THE ARMY

. . . I had to put on my uniform, and stand freezing outside the barracks, waiting for the Captain.

AS A CIVILIAN

. . . I dress as I please, and stand freezing at the railroad station, waiting for the 8:36.

IN THE ARMY

. . . I had to rub elbows with my entire platoon at breakfast, and had to eat what everyone else ate.

AS A CIVILIAN

. . . I breakfast at a friendly drugstore near my office, and I eat whatever I feel like eating.

IN THE ARMY

. . . if I were late for duty, I'd get chewed out by the Captain.

AS A CIVILIAN

. . . I get to the office when I please. No one checks on me.

IN THE ORDERLY ROOM

. . . I had to lick the Colonel's boots when he came to inspect.

IN THE AD AGENCY

. . . I bow to no one. The client comes to me with humble requests.

AS A P.F.C.

. . . I always had the feeling that the other P.F.C.s were trying to beat me out of my Corporal's promotion.

AS AN ACCOUNT EXECUTIVE

. . . I feel secure in my job. No one is after it. I know I'll be moved up fairly, on my own merit.

IN THE ARMY

... whenever I'd get an official memo, I'd always be scared it was a transfer to some distant outpost . . .

IN THE AD AGENCY

... whenever I get my pay envelope, I open it with confidence, knowing that all is well . . .

ARMY LIFE DROVE ME NUTS
. . . so I left the service the first chance I got and became a civilian.

IN CIVILIAN LIFE
. . . my experience is in demand. I know I can always get a job with another firm.

Shopping Dept.

SUPER-DUPER MARKETS

FORCE-OUT-THE-SMALL-RETAIL-GROCER

GALA SALE

SAVE ON MEAT AND MILK
LIVE COWS ea. $1.98

FINEST QUALITY
HORSEMEAT

THOROUGHBRED WINNERS	HARNESS WINNERS	LOSERS
lb. 84c	lb. 69c	lb. 02c

SKINLESS AND BONELESS
LIZARDS ea. 27c

IMPORTED PICKLED TENTACLES OF
OCTOPUS per tentacle 25c

READY-TO-EAT SMOKED FILLETS OF
ARMADILLO per filet 85c

LEG OF LAMB lb. 94c
ARM OF LAMB lb. 84c
SHOULDER OF LAMB lb. 74c
REST OF LAMB lb. 01c

ECONOMICAL
280 lb. bag of Chicken Flickings 13c

PIG'S KNUCKLES 10 for 24c
PIG'S BRASS KNUCKLES per set 98c
BUM STEERS lb. 37c
DOUBLE CROSSERS ea. 12c

FRESH, TASTY
VIRGINIA HAM lb. 84c

DARING, RACY
CYNTHIA HAM QU-2-9970

FANCY TUNA can 43c
NOT-SO-FANCY TUNA can 33c
SLOPPY TUNA can 03c

GARDEN FRESH
BIRDBATH WATER qrt. bottle 18c

HEALTHFUL
FROZEN BRILLO 20 pads for 39c

½ lb. Print Butter 23c
½ lb. Linotype Butter 33c
½ lb. Offset Butter 43c

LARGE ECONOMY SIZE JAR OF
INSTANT WATER JUST ADD HOT COFFEE 85c

EARLY GARDEN PEAS can 02c
LATE GARDEN PEAS can 22c
LATE, LATE GARDEN PEAS chan. 2

New Green Cabbage head 07c
Old Purple Cabbage head 27c

BELLY-BUTTON LINT oz. 68c

LUSH
STEWED PRUNES vat 69

SEDATE
SOBER PRUNES bag 09c

CORN ON THE COB ea. 22c
COB WITHOUT THE CORN 72c

(Prices subject to change if you don't watch our clerks carefully)

LITERARY MOVIE DEPT.

Morbid Dick

CHARACTERS IN MELVIN'S GREAT NOVEL COME ALIVE IN MOVIE VERSION

WHO CAN FORGET the famous climax of "Morbid Dick" when Captain Aslob (bearing striking resemblance to Abe Lincoln) demonstrates the fine old art of whale splitting.

"Call me Fishmeal!"

WITH THESE OMINOUS WORDS, "Morbid Dick" begins as we see Fishmeal wending way over rugged countryside looking for New Bedford, Mass. He has hard time finding it . . . since picture is being shot in Ireland.

Queeg-Queeg, Ex-Cannibal

NEXT WE MEET Queeg-Queeg, ex-Cannibal turned Harpooner, who speaks with odd Middle-European accent. He has been wandering around New Bedford trying to sell his head but gives up the idea because, without it, his aim would be poor.

Father Maplesyrup, Ex-Sea Captain

EX-SEA CAPTAI[illegible] Maplesyrup, who turned preacher after los[illegible]his ship when it rammed through rear of church, delivers sermon on Jonah and whale from bow-sprit pulpit. Right off, they give away whole plot.

Starstruck, the First Mate

DISGRUNTLED at supporting part he has to play, Peckwad's first mate, Mr. Starstruck, fails in attempt to stir up crew, change plot, turn picture into another "Mutiny on the Bounty" with him in Clark Gable role.

Various Sad-Faced Women

LOCAL IRISH WOMENFOLK, used as extras to represent sad-faced New Bedford wives bidding men goodbye, are actually members of local Barry Fitzgerald Fan Club conned into lining up on quay in anticipation of his arrival by seaplane.

CAPTAIN ASLOB FINALLY

TENSE SCENE comes when Captain Aslob finally appears on quarterdeck.

TENSION MOUNTS as he offers coin to first man who spots Morbid Dick.

MAKES AN APPEARANCE

TENSION IS UNBEARABLE as he nails coin to mast as incentive.

TENSION IS SUDDENLY RELIEVED as he misses, slams thumb with hammer.

WHALE HUNT,

STORMS,

HOT TEMPERS, BUILD

TO STORY'S CLIMAX

MORTALLY WOUNDED BY HARPOONS imbedded in thick hide, ordinary black whale drags dories over waves in wild maneuver known as "Nantucket Sleigh-Ride", clearly indicating origin of modern sport of water skiing.

AS WILD TYPHOON engulfs ship, crew scrambles into rigging, not to furl sails but to get fifty-yardarm seats for showdown between axe-aiming Star-struck and harpoon-hefting Aslob, with St. Elmo's fire sparking things.

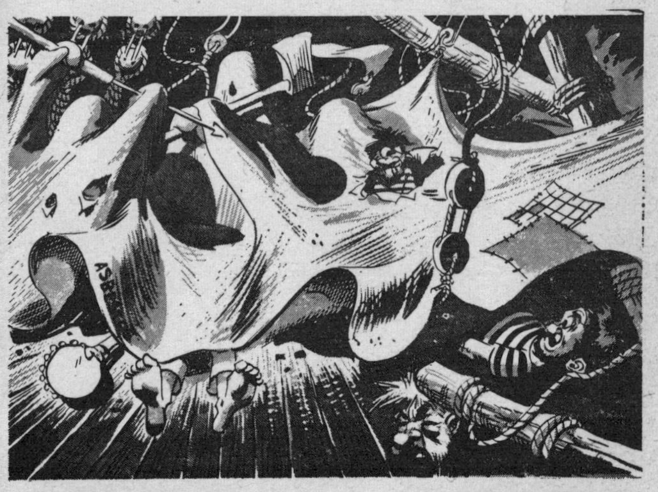

HOWEVER, WATER-LOGGED SAIL, torn loose by raging storm, falls to deck where mutinous first mate is squaring off with stubborn Captain and quickly ends fight by dropping wet blanket on whole furshlugginer proceeding.

MORBID CLIMAX (when White Whale is at last engaged, when Captain Aslob is dragged to watery grave, when Peckwad is rammed and sunk, when entire crew save Fishmeal, drowns) created baffling technical problem for film makers. Problem being: who's gonna take whale's part?

After trying several promising whales, problem of casting Morbid Dick was solved by using disguised World War II surplus blimp. However, as is obvious in above scene, problem was not entirely solved.

COMPARISON PROVES DEPT.

Did you ever stop to wonder where advertisers get those "*ordinary* detergents", or those "*other* leading cigarettes", or those "just *plain* soaps", they use for comparison, in order to demonstrate the superiority of their own brands? Did you? Well, we stopped to wonder! Then we had our

PROD
or TV Com

"Products for TV Commercials, Inc." manufactures dulling "ordinary" liquid

massive research staff do some checking. And here is what she came up with: The entire market has been insidiously cornered by a little-publicized, multi-million dollar operation known as:

UCTS

mercials, Inc.

shampoo used to demonstrate how much cleaner and brighter Halo gets your hair.

One product always in demand is
that inferior tire which blows to pieces

when it rides over those spikes while
he Goodrich Life-Saver holds together.

Popular items manufactured by thi
million-dollar company are the little "A's'

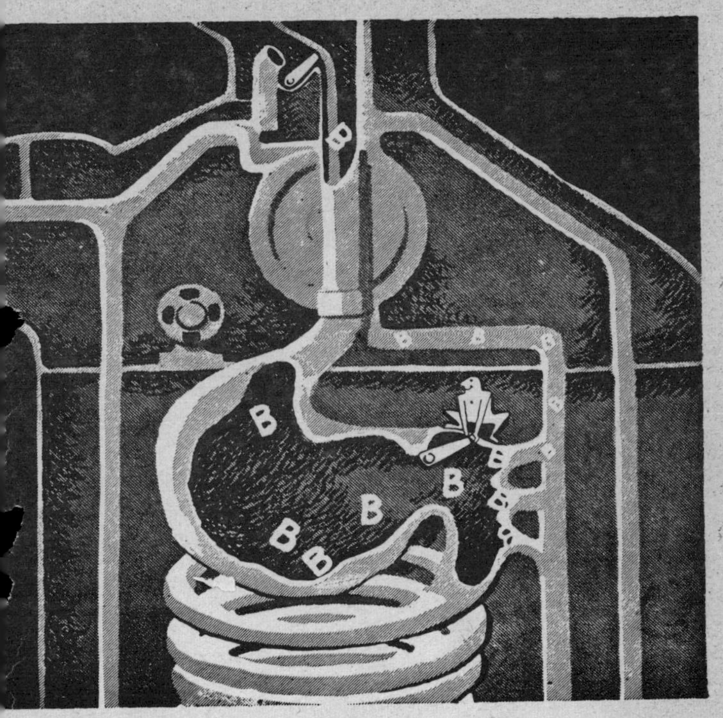

which take so long to get into the bloodstream
mpared to Bufferin's "B's".

Another vital item turned out by this little-known company is that clumsy auto-

mobile which doesn't quite make a U-turn in the space the Nash Rambler takes.

Mr. Aristotle Q. Axolotl, genial Chairman of the Board of "Products for TV Commercials, Inc.", shown with some of the "ordinary" items his multi-million dollar company manufactures. "I hate to brag," says Mr. Axolotl, "but our products are so ***inferior,*** *they're guaranteed to make any advertiser's mediocre brand look absolutely fabulous by comparison!"*

OH, PROMISE ME DEPT.

Another journalistic "First" from the brave, intrepid, slightly jaded editors of MAD: Never-before-published snapshots from a

WEDDING ALBUM

(with follow-up shots taken six months later) . . .

THE BRIDE DRESSING . . .

SIX MONTHS LATER . . .

THE FATHER GIVES AWAY THE BRIDE...

SIX MONTHS LATER...

THE WEDDING RINGS...

SIX MONTHS LATER...
PAWNS
NOT AXOLOTL A
JOXL X. OSSZEFOGVA prop.

THROWING RICE . . .

SIX MONTHS LATER . . .

THE FIRST WALTZ . . .

SIX MONTHS LATER . . .

THE WEDDING CAKE...

SIX MONTHS LATER...

KISSING THE BRIDE . . .

SIX MONTHS LATER . . .

ADULT WESTERN DEPT.

ACROSS THE THRESHOLD . . .

SIX MONTHS LATER . . .

GUNSMOKED

This here is Boot Hill. Many men are buried here. Some 'cause they were good, some 'cause they were bad. But all, 'cause they were dead, by George!

y name's Madd Dillinger. I'm eSoto City's U.S. Marshal. I'm sponsible for puttin' most of ese men here in Boot Hill. Yuh e, I'm also DeSoto ity's grave-digger.

Every week, I come up here t Boot Hill, take off m' hat, look down, an' remember a story from the old days in DeSoto City. I look down an' I remember the story 'cause I got the script hid right here in the sweatband!

"THE STORY I RECOLLECT JUST NOW IS ABOU THIS PORE OL' GUNMAN DOWN AT THE LAS STRAW SALOON. THE TROUBLE HE HAD WA.

HE WAS ONE O' THEM PSYCHOPATHS, Y'KNOW? GOSH HE SURE DID HAVE A PASSEL O' SYNDROMES . . ."

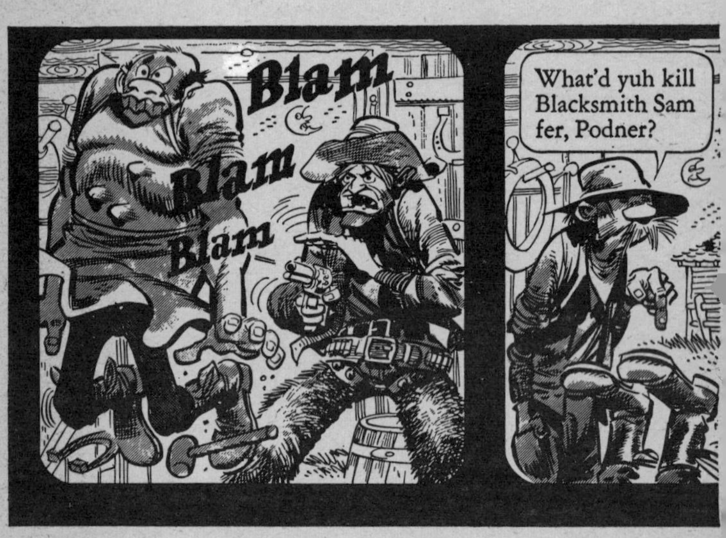
Blam
Blam
Blam
What'd yuh kill Blacksmith Sam fer, Podner?

He put a new et of shoes n mah hoss!
So what's wrong with puttin' a new set of shoes on yore hoss?
They wuz *blue suede* shoes!

Marshal Dillinger! Marshal Dillinger! You've come back to town at last!
That's right, Chestnut! Who got kilt while I wuz gone?

Wa'al, Gambler Dan got kilt in the Last Straw saloon yestiddy . . . an' Blacksmith Sam got kilt in the livery stable las' night. . . . an'. . .

Hey, how come you fix it so's yore always out of town when these killin's happen, Marshal Dillinger? Hah? How come?
Can't stand the sight of blood!

"I DECIDED TO WAIT FOR THIS PORE KILLER DOWN BY THE LAST STRAW. ALL MY FRIENDS WAS THERE. . . ."

Say, Kiddie, how come if'n yore a Café entertainer, I never see yuh singin' or dancin'?
That's cause yore always out of town Marshal . . .
How many times I gotta ask yuh not t' pay me off in gold dust? Makes my stockin' lumpy!

"AND THEN—HE SHOWED, AND WE HAD A REAL ADULT SHOWDOWN. I REMEMBER IT WELL, 'TWAS JUST AFORE THE LAST COMMERCIAL. . . ."

...an' I drew me a bead ...an' I squeezed on the trigger... an'...

Better hand over yore gun, Podner. How come yuh kilt Blacksmith Sam an' Gambler Dan, an' *Mayor Melvin?*

HOLLYWOOD DEPT. II:

ANOTHER SCENE WE'D LIKE TO SEE

The Faithful Dog

HELP!

DOG CATCHER
JOE Orlando

BUSINESS DEPT.

How many times have you picked up your favorite newspaper, finished the comics, and then read something like this . . .

Atlas Ho

Osszefogva, May 10th. Edgar Frimp, president of the Atlas Paper Clip Co., was honored today for 25 years of service with his firm. Frimp started with Atlas in 1932

Yes, it's a familiar story. But have you ever asked yourself how it really happens? Everyone is interested in how men like Edgar Frimp reached the top . . . so here, in his own own words, is Edgar J. Frimp's . . .

$UCCE$$

nors Edgar Frimp

as an office boy, and worked his way up to his present executive position.

When asked the secret of his success, Frimp said:

"I owe it all to diligence, integrity, and faith that a man can climb to the top by just plain good honest hard work."

Frimp further elaborated on his formula for success

"My first job with Atlas was as an office boy. There were fifty other applicants for the job, but I won out over all of them . . ."

"Next, I heard of an opening as a clerk. It boiled down to a choice between me and this other fellow. I worked hard to outshine him . . ."

"Much of my success I owe to Miss Thelma Hendershot, who was head of personnel at the time. Miss Thelma took an interest in me . . ."

Miss Hendershot recognized my potential immediately, and soon I
as promoted to Chief Clerk. This gave me added responsibility . . ."

"But I had my eye on my next goal, the Vice-Presidency. Discreetly I conferred with my superiors to determine what my chances were . . .'

"And before long, the job was mine. I worked hard at my position as Vice-President of Atlas, establishing good will with customers . . ."

"I never let my executive status go to my head. I always manage to remain friendly with my old colleagues who were still clerks . . .

"I never really wanted to be President. I remember how I used to tell everyone that the current President was doing a fine job . . ."

"But despite my objections, the position of top man was thrust upon me. I then set about increasing the efficiency of the firm . . ."

"Today, I have the right people in the right jobs, and our company is moving ahead, ever upward on to its rightful place in industry."

BASE BALL'S

QUENTIN SCURVY
1ST BASEMAN, CLEVELAND, A.L.
1927-1938
VOTED LEAST VALUABLE PLAYER IN AMERICAN LEAGUE 8 YEARS IN ROW. SET RECORD IN 1938 FOR BEING THROWN OUT OF LEADING HOTEL IN EVERY AMERICAN LEAGUE CITY. NOTORIOUS FOR DRUNKEN DRIVING, DISORDERLY CONDUCT, ASSAULT AND BATTERY. FINISHED PLAYING CAREER WITH SING SING LIFERS OF THE SOLITARY LEAGUE.

HALL OF SHAME

CHESTER RIPP
SHORTSTOP, ST. LOUIS, A.L.
1929-1938
BENCHED 28 TIMES IN JULY, 1935, BECAUSE OF HANGNAIL. HOLDS RECORD FOR SPIKING SAME SECOND BASEMAN SIX TIMES IN GAME WITH WASHINGTON, JUNE 16, 1936. DELIBERATELY INFECTED ENTIRE TEAM WITH WHOOPING COUGH DURING SERIES WITH CLEVELAND, JULY 3-5, 1934.

BORIS DUCKBILL
UMPIRE, N.L.
1931-1932
HOLDS RECORD FOR BEING HIT BY 35 DIFFERENT BRANDS OF SODA-POP BOTTLES IN ONE GAME. ONLY UMPIRE TO RECEIVE 8 SEEING-EYE DOGS AS GIFTS IN ONE SEASON. ENDED CAREER BY BEING TRAMPLED BY ANGRY FANS AFTER GAME BETWEEN CINCINNATI AND PITTSBURGH, SEPTEMBER 3, 1932.

ONLY PITCHER TO MISTAKE RESIN BAG FOR BASEBALL IN 3 CONSECUTIVE ODD-NUMBERED INNINGS. IN 1952, SET RECORD BY BEING ACCUSED OF THROWING SPITTER 651 TIMES. HOLDS ALL-TIME RECORD FOR WILD PITCHES. IN 1950, BEANED SAME SPECTATOR 5 TIMES. STARTED 265 MAJOR LEAGUE GAMES; NEVER PITCHED A STRIKE.

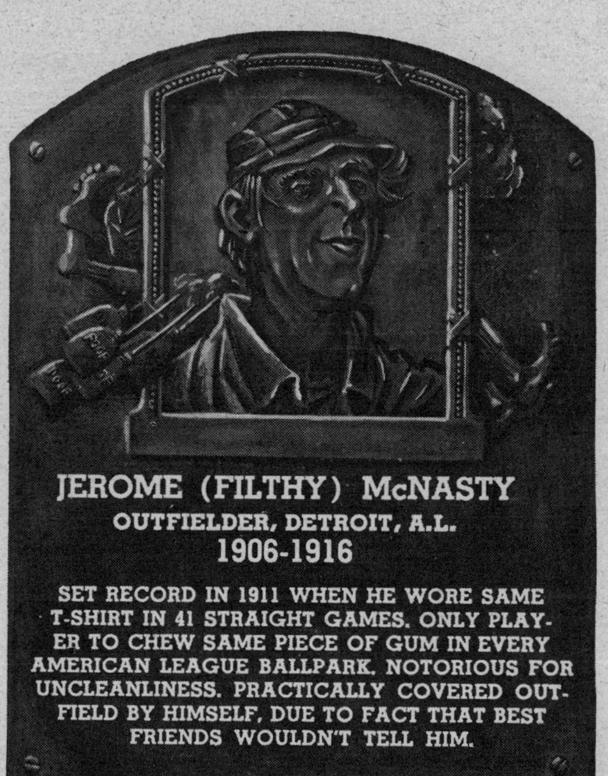
JEROME (FILTHY) McNASTY
OUTFIELDER, DETROIT, A.L.
1906-1916
SET RECORD IN 1911 WHEN HE WORE SAME T-SHIRT IN 41 STRAIGHT GAMES. ONLY PLAYER TO CHEW SAME PIECE OF GUM IN EVERY AMERICAN LEAGUE BALLPARK. NOTORIOUS FOR UNCLEANLINESS. PRACTICALLY COVERED OUTFIELD BY HIMSELF, DUE TO FACT THAT BEST FRIENDS WOULDN'T TELL HIM.

SOAMES GRULNIK

VENDOR, PHILADELPHIA, N.L.

1942-1947

CARRIED WORST SELECTION OF CANDY BARS IN ANY BALLPARK, 1943. HOLDS RECORD FOR SHORTCHANGING 85 FANS DURING GAME WITH ST. LOUIS, APR. 29, 1946. BLOCKED VIEW OF MORE THRILLING PLAYS IN SEASON THAN ANY OTHER VENDOR, 1944. BANNED FROM ALL BALLPARKS, 1947, FOR SELLING FLAT BEER.

ALFRED E. (SMILEY) NEUMAN

BATBOY, NEW YORK, N.L.

1893-1949

WIDELY KNOWN FOR HIS GREAT USELESSNESS AND INEFFICIENCY. WAS MISTAKEN FOR BASEBALL BAT IN GAME WITH BROOKLYN, 1923, AND HIT INTO TRIPLE PLAY. GOT LOST IN GRANDSTAND, PITTSBURGH, 1927, AND WAS NOT FOUND FOR FIVE YEARS. FINALLY TURNED UP AS PRIZE IN BOX OF CRACKERJACKS.

HAVING A BALL DEPT.

TO: Smurdville High School
FROM: The Editors of MAD
RE: Invitation to Spring Dance

We of MAD sincerely appreciate being invited to your first Annual Spring Dance. Had we been asked as "guests" instead of "clean-up crew" we might even have accepted. Actually, though,

PLACE TO HOLD AFFAIR IS FINALLY SELECTED after weeks of wrangling among Student Social Committee, by school prin-

we have no desire to attend. Because our publisher once went to high school, and he told us all about the fiasco known as a...

cipal, who pulls rank. Strangely, his choice is same as it's been for past 19 years . . . smelly old school gym!

DATE IS SET, TICKETS ARE PRINTED, and problem of selling them is taken on by school "Boosters"., members of football team, and assorted "con-men". Each group uses own successful method of "Friendly Persuasion" to do the job.

BRAIN
(The school "Con-Men")

BROAD

(The school "Boosters")

BRAWN

(The school Football Team)

THREE FACULTY MEMBERS ARE CAREFULLY CHOSEN TO KEEP THINGS RUNNING RIGHT

MISS AIDA SOTO VOCE, Music Teacher, is given job of selecting music to be played at dance . . . chooses 13 waltzes, 4 minuets, 2 gavottes and a Charleston.

MR. OZGOOD Z'BEARD, Gym Teacher, is given assignment to maintain order by judicious use of modern psychology, tactful diplomacy, and mainly muscles.

MR. HY OCTANE, Chem Teacher, who has experience with the baser elements at school, is given job of seeing that punch bowl contains only grape juice.

MUSIC IS PROVIDED BY . . .

. . . the "Off-Beats", a group of students who refused to join the school band, much to the relief of the Music Director. Their title well-describes the rhythms they play . . .

GYM DECOR IS SUPPLIED BY . . .

FINALLY, THE BIG NIGHT ARRIVES. The crowd is jammed to the walls. Well, actually, the crowd is jammed *against*

. . . a "Decorations Committee" of artistically endowed students. Unfortunately, even after long tireless efforts at camouflage . . . it still looks like smelly old school gym!

the walls . . . and the basketball court is "no-man's land". Even school "make-out" men haven't the nerve to cross it.

AFTER A WHILE, THE GIRLS come to the realization that, if there's gonna be a dance at all, somebody will have to take the initiative. So the braver among them select partners, move out into "no-man's land", and begin to dance . . .

NATURALLY, NO ONE DANCES WITH THE PARTNER they'd *really* like to dance with, for fear of starting those em-

KICK ME

AFTER A WHILE, THE BOYS come to the realization that, if they're gonna follow the girls' example, this dance is gonna be one big flop. A conference is called on a plan of action . . . and one brave youth volunteers to break the ice.

barassing "John loves Mary" rumors. So everyone winds up more or less mismatched, and those rumors start anyway . . .

DANCE BEGINS TO LIVEN UP AS STUDENTS

CHEM TEACHER Octane, who has been studiously guarding that punch-bowl, fails to notice the strange goings-on around the water-cooler all night.

MUSIC TEACHER Sotto Voce, having developed a sudden, intense thirst, fails to notice that "My Hero" sounds oddly like "Rock Around the Clock."

GYM TEACHER Z'BEARD, who had climbed rope to get bird's-eye-view of proceedings, fails to notice that route down has been cleverly removed.

FUN BEGINS WHEN CHEM TEACHER, standing at punchbowl all evening, finally collapses from drinking it all.

FUN CONTINUES AS GYM TEACHER spots the activity around the water cooler and attempts to slide down rope.

FUN GOES ON AS MUSIC TEACHER dances with star football player to prove that she is one of the gang. Reputation vanishes following day when she flunks the poor clod.

FUN REACHES PINNACLE WHEN GWENDOLYN FURD, self-appointed entertainer, gargles with water before singing. Lyrics to "Because" strangely resemble shady sailor song.

HIGHLIGHT OF EVENING COMES WHEN

ECHOES OF MELEE RESULT IN POLICE RAID

nd another Smurdville High Spring Dance comes to an

END

MAD, BECAUSE IT STRONGLY BELIEVES IN TRUTH ...BECAUSE IT STRONGLY BELIEVES IN SINCERITY ...AND MAINLY BECAUSE IT STRONGLY BELIEVES IN GETTIN' EVEN, BY GEORGE, NOW GETS EVEN WITH THE KIND OF THING WE FELL FOR THE OTHER DAY...

REAL ESTATE ADS

EVERY SUNDAY MORNING, like clockwork, members of Furd family leap from bed, dress frantically, gulp breakfast, and scramble for the real estate ads.

YES, FURDS long to move to the suburbs. They long for elbow room. They long for breathing space. But mostly, they long to get their hearing back . . .

SEEMS FURDS go through clockwork Sunday ritual because they're sick of living in cramped clock-tower apartment amid ear-splitting chiming clockworks.

LIVE IN THE LAP OF LUXURY . . . and in the grip of a mortg

at Painan Acres

Introducing the fabulous "Monaco Ranger" —Prince of Ranch Houses!

Only $14,999

(Which looks cheaper than $15,000!)

No Down Payment for VETS

(They pay FULL price cash!)

COME OUT TODAY!

DIRECTIONS: Go straight out Route 26 to traffic circle, then turn left and . . . No, wait! Take the Turnpike to Exit 12, go South one mile and . . . No, that's no good either. Drive down Old Miller Parkway to . . . to . . . You know what? You can't get out here from where you are!

. . . a sparkling interpretation of luxurious suburban living in strong red brick, sturdy brown fieldstone and soft green wood, in an unsurpassed location on the North Shore, near beautiful Heartburn Hills, with an unobstructed view of the gasworks, and only a short walking distance from the city dump.

PAINAN ACRES is another ALFR

e . . .

Rendering by Jack Kamen

FEATURING SUCH ARCHITECTURAL TRIUMPHS AS:

- a front door
- an All-Electric Kitchen, which will give you the shock of your life.
- an especially wide but unexpectedly not deep enough garage.
- a 37 foot Sunken Living Room with 37 foot Ladder included.
- a 6 foot Picture Window with your choice of picture.
- a spacious basement for rainy day activities like swimming and boating.
- Plus countless extras for Pleasant and Comfortable Modern Living . . .
- all extra of course!

FIRST SECTION COMPLETELY SOLD OUT!

(Which leaves us with this other house to get rid of!)

E. NEUMAN atrocity.

FURDS IN FAMILY FORD FIGHT

UNBELIEVABLE REAL ESTATE AD sends eager house-hunting Fu forth in family Ford to battle brawling Sunday traffic compo chiefly of other eager house-hunting families sent forth by ot unbelievable real estate ads. A crazy mixed-up mess, by Geo

FENDER TO FENDER FRACAS

NOTE DISMAY etched on faces of Furd Family. Dismay however, is not caused by the traffic delay. Dismay is caused by sight of destination: real look of house cleverly illustrated in unbelievable real estate ad.

A MODERN FACTORY WILL BE ERECTED ON THIS SITE

Final realization finally comes to furious Furds that some real estate ads depict very unreal estates. Furds realize now that stretching out house in ad is insidious trick of builder calculated to deceive prospective buyers into thinking they are getting fantastic big house at ridiculous small price. Furds' retaliation at this deception consists of insidious trick of stretching out builder. (see left)

END

SOFT-SELL ADVERTISING DEPT. II:

One more example of Madison Avenue's new sick-making, soft-sell approach—and then it's good-bye.

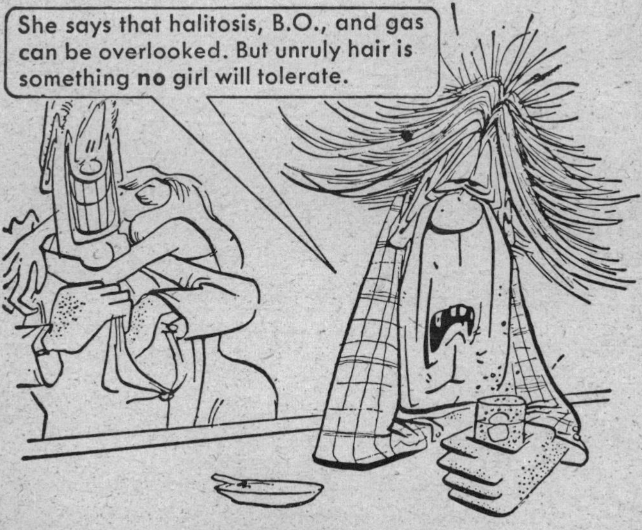

She says that halitosis, B.O., and gas can be overlooked. But unruly hair is something **no** girl will tolerate.

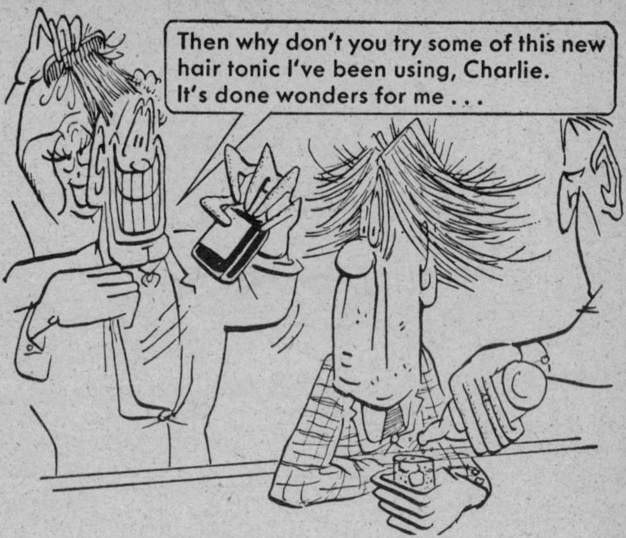

Then why don't you try some of this new
hair tonic I've been using, Charlie.
It's done wonders for me . . .

Why, that's the most amazing hair tonic I ever drank!

That's because you mixed it with **this,** Charlie! Schveppes Activated Sparkling Seltzer! Any drink is amazing when it's mixed with **SCHVEPPES!**
EPPES

Why, I wouldn't drink my Hair Tonic with any other mixer but **SCHVEPPES!**
It goes great with **STERNO,** too!
Remember: **SCHVEPPES** is activated!